In search of the

Gold of the Desert Kings™

A Journal of my Travels

EAGLE'S FLIGHT™

Learning that Powers Performance.

1-800-567-8079
Worldwide 519-767-1747
www.eaglesflight.com

Learning that Powers Performance.

1-800-567-8079
Worldwide 519-767-1747
www.eaglesflight.com

Dedicated to Roz, Sabrina, Sean
and Mom and Dad;
in appreciation of their unwavering
love and support.

"Some trust in chariots, and some in horses:
but we will remember the name of the Lord our God"
Psalm 20:7

A chronicle of my adventures...
...and of my life
changing learnings.

In search of the
Gold of the Desert Kings™

NOTE TO SELF—

I intend to annotate this journal to capture and note my observations in order that I may profit — in more ways than one — from this incredible experience. I shall jot down some of my learnings on this left hand side, and chronicle my adventures over on the right hand side.

January

In my research on early Mesopotamia, I have come across numerous references to an ancient gold mine and storehouse, high in the hills of Rakar.

Apparently several centuries ago the kings who ruled those desert lands decided to store their wealth in a single location; one that was therefore more easily protected than several smaller sites, had they each created their own storehouse.

I suspect it was probably also a convenient way to watch one another!

Unfortunately the ways of the eternal desert defeated them, for a sandstorm of unprecedented fury raged for eight months after they moved their gold to the mountains.

January (continued...)

The way to the mountains was lost; the desert now much larger; and the peril crossing it much greater.

They tried to return - but died doing so, and were buried there in a place known as the Tomb of Kings. A fearsome and forbidding place by all accounts - and one avoided by even the fearless desert nomads.

I now intend to go and cross this desert for myself, and so recover the Gold of the Desert Kings.

The First Monday in March

Well, I have made my way to a village on the outskirts of what I now realize to be a vast and perilous desert. This place will serve as home base for me, as it seems to be able to provide the basic necessities for such an adventure as I propose.

It is not inhospitable - moreover once my intentions were made clear I find myself the topic of a constant source of discussion. Apparently I am not the first to make such a trip!

I must learn more.

Early on I got information but did not know how much value to give it at the time. I should have been more disciplined to examine it more thoroughly.

3 STEPS:
* Gather information.
* Once it's all together, go back and assess relative value.
* Then take appropriate action.

These were hard lessons to have learned!

Tuesday

While haggling over the price of some figs
with a local vendor, I was approached by a
well-to-do tentmaker. He has given me to
understand that several others have set out
on a similar quest without his tents, and
learned, to their dismay, how unforgiving is
this vast and unyielding sea of golden sand.
I pressed him for more detail.

It seems that previously some have successfully
found their way to the treasure mines in the
mountains - and returned. Alive. This was
most heartening.

I failed to give new
information due consideration.
Beware of pride!

Tuesday (continued...)

It also seems that as many more were never heard from or seen again - but the buzzard population is, from what I understand, much larger here than what would be considered normal. This is most discouraging.

It may well be wise to consider acquiring one of his fine products. I shall be giving this considerable thought.

I shall name him Lawrence!

Wednesday

Today I was able to acquire a camel! They are very different from what I had expected. Their odor is quite strong; and it appears they themselves are equally strong, and able to carry a great deal. I see this as most advantageous as I intend to have a great deal of gold with me to bring back! I shall name him Lawrence.

I am coming to appreciate this village more each day. It is actually very well off - they have many of the amenities one would like but not expect (Herbert's Heavenly Honey for one). The people are well educated and courteous. I almost get the impression they have a source of wealth that goes beyond that which comes from the obvious tourism in the area.

① **Teamwork** is a powerful advantage when you all share a common goal.

② Be driven by your **own** strategies, not those of others!

Wednesday (continued...)

On that point, several very interesting individuals seem to be here for much the same purpose - although it mystifies me how they heard of the mines. I'm considering joining up with some of them; I've a feeling that I'd do better with more heads than just mine.

I suppose there will be several parties making a run for it shortly. Perhaps I should step up my pace a bit - they all seem quite enthusiastic to be gone, and my new acquaintances and I are beginning to worry about being left behind, and so possibly returning less profitably than the other groups.

We took far longer to get ready
than we should have!

Greater:

① Intensity
② Focus on the task at hand
            ... was needed.

Have a sense of urgency!

Thursday

We're beginning to kit out for our adventure.
My, there's a lot to purchase! And our combined
resources - while far greater than what we
each have individually - still seem only
barely adequate. But we shall be able to
acquire the necessities. But alas, none of
Herbert's Heavenly Honey.

This is becoming more involved than I had
foreseen. The desert is not something to be
taken lightly, I'm learning. And to make
matters worse - within a month all travel
will become impossible, or so we've all been
told by the locals. Apparently a season the
locals call "khamsin" will arrive with such
severity that it is imperative that we be back
from our adventure before its arrival.

There appears to be some key principles of effective teams. I've now identified two of them:

① Unanimous focus on a common goal.

② Enthusiastic effort from all participants.

Thursday (continued...)

I have learned that khamsin is an extended period of unrelenting, intense wind and sandstorms; and that ancient legends speak of a particularly harsh khamsin causing the demise of the original Desert Kings!

My task is growing more daunting each hour! But the gold beckons - and I shall persevere.

Thank goodness for my new-found companions.

TEAMWORK

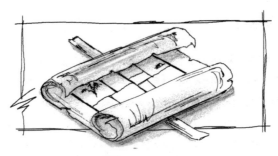

Planning

In hindsight we did a poor job of planning. My key learnings from this phase are:

1. <u>Put more time into planning</u> — I was preoccupied far too much with my surroundings and not enough with my mission.

2. <u>Gather more data</u> — we went out far too underequipped with regards to information.

3. <u>Do not let enthusiasm override adequate and considered planning.</u>

Friday

We are finally getting ready to go, which delights me. My fellow adventurers are very pleased with Lawrence - apparently he is an exceptionally fine animal - although I cannot in good conscience take credit for this particular bit of good fortune.

Another bit of good news: one of our group has acquired a map of the entire region. This is indeed excellent! We spent last evening immersed in dark tea, figs, and discussion; poring over the map to plan our route.

Remain focused on the
task at hand.

Avoid getting sidetracked!

Friday (continued...)

We are progressing nicely. One thing however continues to concern me: there are several other groups also kitting out here, many I feel more ready to leave than are we. Time is against us all, so it pays to keep an eye on them. I should hate to lose out because others have gotten there before us. I sense the need for haste now.

One other thing that has been bothering me is the relative affluence of this small village community. Now I have the answer, and it has caused my desire for haste to greatly increase!

It transpires that the secret of the mountain gold is not as well kept as I had supposed. These villagers have seen adventurers before, as each year at this time there is a brief window before the khamsin, when this vast desert has some tolerance for trespassers. Others have returned - with gold!

I knew capacity was a limiting factor - but failed to give it due consideration in my excitement. Do NOT let enthusiasm override adequate and considered planning. This is a key point regarding planning!

Friday (continued...)

But their capacity is limited - as is ours - by that which they can carry. However once the gold is brought in, these enterprising villages have found a way to sell it for a reasonable profit. And so they have become quite successful as traders of this precious commodity.

Unfortunately their buyers' demand is limited, so the price they will pay us will diminish as supply increases. The sooner we are back - assuming we survive, something becoming more and more of a preoccupation with me - the more we will make. It appears that even here the law of supply and demand is in effect.

And so - we must hurry!

Pride often inhibits reason.

Saturday

A major victory for me today!

The seller of tents has been harassing me ever since my arrival. Can you imagine - needing a tent in the desert! And I've been successful in convincing my colleagues the exorbitant price he's asking is ridiculous. They have - finally - agreed. So I feel quite proud of myself. I've saved us considerable money and rid myself of that pesky and persistent haggler once and for all.

There is a rumor circulating of a very old, some say doddering and senile, old man who has traveled the desert all his life. It seems he has returned again, as is his want, well in advance of the khamsin. It occurred to me he may be able to give us some advice - given the vast extent of his experience.

We spent so long in the village anyway — I could have used my time better by doing both things simultaneously: planning and provisioning while at the same time gathering and assessing information.

I was too quick to disregard this possible value. I should have tested it.

Test information to determine VALUE!

DON'T ASSUME!

Saturday (continued...)

But I've noticed few others have spoken with him; and on searching out his whereabouts I met many who cautioned me with respect to my expectations – he is, by all consents, extremely laborious of speech and manner. If he is indeed so slow, then what value can he really be?

I've decided the time could be better spent focusing on what is now our clear objective: leave immediately, successfully find the mountains, and return with gold, before those whom I have now come to see as our competitors accomplish a similar task. We must be back first! This has become our imperative.

We have a few more necessities to gather, and then we can be off! I must say, despite the looming dangers and the unknown, I'm growing increasingly excited. If I can but get used to Lawrence's unique odor I'm sure all else will fall in line.

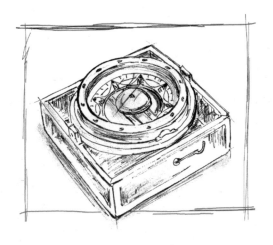

VALIDATE ASSUMPTIONS!

(I never seem to learn this principle!)

Sunday

Whew - we have narrowly avoided a near catastrophe!

While searching the bazaar for some last minute things - chief among them mustache wax - I discovered an out of the way location - little frequented - and occupied by vendors of the less popular items. My fancy was immediately taken by a beautiful mahogany box, housing a large and gleaming brass compass. Surely such an item would be a necessity for us. I can't imagine how I could have overlooked such an obvious piece of necessary equipment.

Acting without a clear
understanding of all the
influencing factors can
be fatal.

① Understand influencing
factors.

② Include them in the plan!

Sunday (continued...)

While chatting with the vendor, I was informed of the vagaries of weather we might encounter. It appears - I was told - that one day may not at all be like another. Sandstorms can come upon one suddenly. And also what they call superheat - a scorching burning fire of a day.

We had not prepared for this. How fortunate we are to have encountered such a learned individual before setting out!

If I'd learned more about what we were facing, it would have been less fearsome.

Planning must include enough to - wherever possible - eliminate the unknown, and at a minimum make provision for all possible eventualities. If we'd done this we would have been far more productive.

Monday

Feeling rather proud of myself, I informed my companions today of my new found information. And in the nick of time, for we've decided to begin our journey at first light tomorrow. An exciting prospect! Soon the Gold of the Desert Kings will be lining our pockets!

But first we must cross what I am learning is surely a fearsome and terrible desert.

Today we will buy the last of our provisions to load on odoriferous Lawrence. I showed our group the compass I purchased on our behalf, explaining (rather more coherently than its vendor I felt) that should we encounter a sandstorm it would keep us from being lost. And far cheaper than the shelter offered by that gouging tent merchant.

Beware of first impressions!

Evaluate based on impact on results, not on appearances.

Monday (continued...)

We have also decided to acquire considerable extra water (poor Lawrence!) to offset the effects of superheat, should we encounter it; and extra food, since I've learned from my worthy compass vendor that during a sandstorm large quantities of food will be ruined. We shall make provision for that. My new friends were rather complimentary regarding the value of my desert wisdom and insight - I was, truthfully, quite flattered in a modest kind of way.

Well, it's grown late, but I'm having trouble sleeping. Tomorrow we're off! Close inspection of our map has shown that there is at least one oasis en route - about four days from here. We shall make first for there.

Time is precious. <u>Every minute</u>
<u>should be used in support of</u>
<u>our objectives</u>. I fear I wasted
considerable amounts of it
early on when I felt we had it
in abundance. I should have
treated time as if it were a
scarce and valuable commodity
right from the start — not
just at the end when we were
approaching the deadline.

Monday (continued...)

My estimate is that we have only 25 days for our journey, nearly half of which will be consumed in travel - both to and from the mountains.

To be out any longer would be to court disaster. Others are already en route, or leaving tomorrow as well. It will be a tight thing - a race, almost, to see who can return, first, with the most.

Despite the hazards, I'm really quite looking forward to the adventure. And am very confident of our ability to excel.

Now I really must try to rest.

Additional key principles of teamwork have emerged. First among these is:

LEADERSHIP!

We failed to identify a leader for our group - the role seemed to be available for any to assume, whenever needed. This did not enhance our focus or our effectiveness.

In the absence of another doing so, I should have put myself forward in this role.

Day 1

It's morning, and a beautiful day in the desert! The sun is high but not too hot. Lawrence seems to be enjoying himself immensely, and smells much better with a warm breeze blowing across the early morning sands. Already the town is out of sight - how quickly these dunes obscure everything - and we can see no other parties, although several left at the same time as did we.

We are appropriately attired, so the sun is not too uncomfortable; well provisioned; and in excellent spirits. I have assumed the task of guiding our progress, so have begun to map out our route.

By nightfall I trust we will be well on our way to becoming rich!

TEAMWORK

A quiet moment at day's end.

Day 1 (continued...)

It's now the evening of what has been a magnificent day. We're nearly bedded down for the night. The party is in excellent spirits; and we regaled one another by the fire tonight with stories of our minor adventures during the day.

I, I'm embarrassed to say, was the source of most of the amusement. Apparently the ladle I'd used all day to drink from was the same one used for Lawrence! They only told this to me tonight after a day of laughter at my unknowing expense.

The sunset was magnificent tonight, casting shades of red across darkened clouds that defy description.

We are keen to begin our day tomorrow, one day closer.

How poorly we used our planning
time at home base, prior to
setting out!

Day 4

What a time of it we've had!

We are, sadly, on our way back to the village. How discouraging!

Two days ago we awoke to a beautiful morning and set out with great hope. By noon the wind had begun to blow quite strongly, and shortly thereafter it picked up, carrying sand with it. Our progress was delayed, for soon we could barely see.

By nightfall we were paralyzed. The howling, rushing wind sounded like a thousand banshees. The sand stung our faces, our hands; penetrated our clothes; found every crack and seam - a million needles over and over. We had no shelter, no respite.

Much of our food was ruined.

Day 4 (continued...)

All the next day the sandstorm howled and raged. We cowered together beside our stoic Lawrence, and waited.

Finally, near the end of that eternal day, the storm abated, and slowly came to an end at sunset. We were in a sea of gold. The evening rays stretched across the endless plains of sand, making virgin and new the world in which we found ourselves. Any trace of our previous passage had long been erased. There was no sound or sign of any others in this whole wide world save ourselves.

Much of our unprotected food was ruined; so we had little to eat; and even now are on strict rations until we successfully return to the village. Fortunately our water was covered or we would surely perish from thirst.

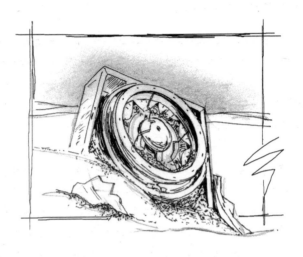

The consequences of poor planning, poor judgement and inadequate information! All could have been easily avoided had I but known the lessons these early days have already taught me.

Day 4 (continued...)

And, worst of all, we feared we were lost. However - I remembered my compass. My compass - hah! This useless artifact will, if we're lucky, just serve to get us home. I now discover it was so poorly made that its inner workings are nearly useless - being as clogged and caked with sand as the rest of us. Its box has seams so large they issued an invitation for the blinding sand to take up permanent residence. Clearly I was misled by the good-for-nothing vendor who insisted I buy the worthless thing.

I've been able to remove enough sand to get a reading and so get us back on track for our return. But now it is completely useless. I'll leave it where we stand as we turn for home - a testament to our discouragement and failure.

UNANIMOUS FOCUS
ON A COMMON GOAL!

This is a key ingredient –
and one which has held
us together. Clearly it is
essential for any team.

Day 5

We made it back late last night - exhausted, discouraged, and yet relieved to be safe. Never has such a small village looked so hospitable.

We have decided to try again.

There is still time.

And so we are quickly trying to re-equip ourselves with the necessary provisions. I believe I shall seek out the fine individual I met earlier who sold those excellent and economical tents, as I believe that he indicated they would shelter us from sandstorms.

We've done some further planning over breakfast and believe that, if we make haste, we can be off again before sunset today and so begin to make up for the time we've lost.

I must hurry.

IDENTIFY RESOURCES!

Day 6

We were in fact able to leave yesterday - but heard some disturbing news from the local vendors: another group was forced to return as well, and they came across the buried remains of a third group who had perished in the storm.

It appears we were lucky.

Today was beautiful and we have made excellent time. A good day's trek is behind us. My map has proved invaluable.

We are on our way again, and are quite encouraged! I have even had time to scratch my name on my own mug, and Lawrence's on his.

We hope to reach an oasis the day after tomorrow, by mid day. I'm sure our faithful Lawrence will be glad of a rest, as will we!

Celebrate successes!

Day 8

How magnificent!

It's late afternoon and I'm sitting in the shade of a tall, leafy palm tree. The breeze is cool, and the sun is just starting to cast long, inviting shadows across the well worn paths of this lush desert oasis.

We've all had the chance to wash and take the sand from our clothes, our hair, and our boots. I even allowed myself the luxury of a shave and a dab of mustache wax. What with my recently acquired tan, clean safari shirt, and pith helmet I do believe I cut quite the dashing figure. All around me are the sounds of several caravans - their camels, pots and pans, shouts, and laughter.

Abundant, cool water.
Tonight, we celebrate life!

Day 8 (continued...)

Clearly they are all as glad as I am to have arrived here safely. Although there is an undercurrent of competition, in this twilight moment the overriding passion for us all is to drink our fill of the abundant and cool water that abounds in this spectacular place, and share stories around the fire. Tomorrow will be time enough to rekindle the desire for gold and wealth; tonight - we celebrate life.

The last 24 hours, while now in the past, still give me cause for some concern. Yesterday we encountered superheat for the first time. Fortunately it lasted - inexplicably - for only a day. But that was enough! We were trudging through an oven - no - a blast furnace and molten iron.

Plan for the unforeseen!

Day 8 (continued...)

Every step was an effort, and we found ourselves having no choice but to stop every hour or so to drink heavily from our water stores - so quickly did we begin to dehydrate. By the end of the day we took stock of our water and were shocked - and considerably dismayed - to realize how low our supplies had shrunk. I'm sure none of us had realized how much we had been consuming during that endless march under the scorching and relentless, unyielding pressure of such burning searing heat. I can only surmise our predicament had we not been so near this glorious oasis with its limitless cool clean water.

That experience has also served as a warning to us all. I'm not entirely sure we had foreseen such a drain on our supplies, and hence have resolved to fill every container - perhaps even my shaving mug! - when we leave, in the event we encounter such heat again.

<u>This we did well –</u>
<u>learning from our experience!</u>
(A very important behavior!)

We are learning more about
teamwork and primarily the
need to <u>split up or share</u>
<u>tasks</u>. It makes us more
<u>efficient</u>. We each have a specific
role, or at least each of the
subgroups do. So my next
principle on teams:
   Create subgroups!

CLEAR ROLES for SUBGROUPS!

Day 8 (continued...)

I've overheard several of the other groups saying much the same thing. Apparently it was deep cause for concern among us all.

Tonight I shall talk to the other groups about the likelihood of its re-occurrence - perhaps some will know more than I. After this last week I'm much more aware of how little we really do know, and how much better equipped we would be - and hence more likely to survive, let alone succeed - if we knew more. Tonight learning all I can will be my personal objective.

TEAMWORK

We approached this expedition with inadequate commitment to maximizing our results. Avoiding the Tomb of Kings cost us several days in the desert.

Our goals <u>should</u> have been:

① To commit to maximizing the results of our efforts

    and <u>then</u>...

② Take appropriate action: in this case - find out how to pass through the Tomb safely. Others did.

<u>My key lesson</u>: focus on maximizing, not just surviving.

Day 9

It is nearly 10 am and we shall soon be off
again. But it was not an easy decision to
continue - we have been discussing and debating
the issue for the last two hours. It was the
proximity of neighboring villages that finally
persuaded us to continue. And our planning.

Last night we learned several things - all
to our dismay. Worst of all, I think, is that
we are but a day's trek from the mysterious
Tomb of Kings. It lies directly between us
and the mountains. The Bedouins who travel
these inhospitable wastelands say it's haunted
by long dead desert rulers; and some even go so
far as to say that those who enter never return!
A ghastly place.

PRODUCTIVITY IS MORE
IMPORTANT THAN ACTIVITY!

The mysterious Tomb of Kings!

We were too easily discouraged,
basing our decisions on too little
information, and really hearsay.
Most unwise!

Day 9 (continued...)

There is a way around it though - the way is longer, but apparently safer. We intend to take that alternate route. Some of the other groups have clearly chosen the more reckless route, and intend to brave those unknown dangers. They seem far less afraid than I believe is healthy. I fear for their safety.

In the spirit of goodwill I took the liberty of mentioning this to them as they loaded their gear this morning - I would not want their deaths on my conscience. But they seemed unperturbed despite my warnings. Oh well. Certainly I am indeed fortunate to be a part of a team that shows such good common sense, and a willingness to listen to reason.

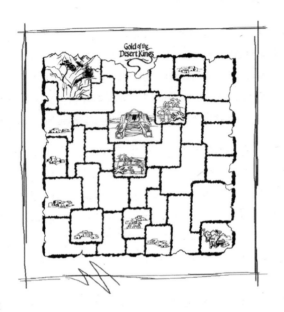

The presence of a safe alternative stood in the way of our determination to excel. We compromised and accepted far less than what was possible.

WE LACKED FOCUS on the goal of achieving all that could be achieved!

Day 9 (continued...)

The other terrifying intelligence we received from many sources was that, as khamsin season approaches, the weather worsens! We will very likely encounter much to fear in that arena. It certainly gave us cause to ponder.

As the argument raged around this issue I must confess I found my mind drifting, and I idly happened to look at the map. I noticed for the first time that there are villages on the western perimeter of this vast desert!

Villages!

I immediately interrupted the discussion to bring home this discovery; and hastened to point out that we had only to always have enough food and water to carry us to the nearest village, and we would be safe! A rather excellent plan even if I do say so myself. That turned the tide, and we agreed to continue.

Another teamwork lesson has
emerged from our discussions:

EFFECTIVE and FREQUENT
COMMUNICATION

Our success in this area has
done much to ensure our survival!

Day 9 (continued...)

And so we're off, with Lawrence bringing up the rear - we've discovered he smells not nearly as badly that way! As we go my companions are in for a pleasant surprise - I traded one of my oak mustache brushes (I had brought two in case one was lost) for an excellent harmonica. I shall play an aria from Vendi's opera "La Traviata" for my colleagues as we go. It will surely serve to buoy our spirits as we make our way to the gold that awaits.

TEAMWORK

Next thing we know, he'll
be completely inside!

Day 10

No sooner had we left camp this morning than we were swallowed up in another raging sandstorm! But... thanks to what I may modestly say to be my own foresight... we weathered it well and continue to make excellent progress.

At the first sign of the coming storm we quickly erected our excellent shelter - quality workmanship in each stitch. It kept out the sand, and left us well protected in every way. We even had room for Lawrence - although we only allowed his nose and head inside. We waited out the worst of it with a small meal and a nap.

As soon as the storm had abated we were able to continue, refreshed, for the rest of the day, and even into the night.

Beware a false sense of security.
This detour cost us time which
could have been spent collecting
gold.

Day 10 (continued...)

The stars are magnificent as they stretch out like sequins over this vast and unpredictable expanse of sand.

Our decision to circumvent the Tomb of Kings has given us some measure of peace (how great is man's fear of the unknown!). But it has slowed us down somewhat. Nonetheless, if all goes well we shall reach the mountains in two more days, if we can keep up this pace.

We've made it!

Day 13

It is early morning, and I am the first among my companions to awake. How glorious is the sunrise, and the cool breezes from the mountains. We have made it! We have arrived!

The last two days have passed in a daze. The sun was hot, but not unbearable - beautiful days in the desert really, so we pushed on long and hard, covering relentlessly mile after mile with little pause.

By yesterday afternoon the mountain peaks were in view - most heartening. Even Lawrence seemed to pick up his pace somewhat. By evening we were at the desert's end, and collapsed, exhausted. We had made it.

And so this morning I awoke excited and refreshed.

Focus on the essentials!

Day 13 (continued...)

I dare not shave as our water supply is precious until we find a fresh source. I shall search for some in the mountains today, but if I fail our supply must hold us until our return. So it is a very precious commodity! I've nonetheless waxed my mustache, dusted off my now faded and tattered pith helmet, and luxuriated in a change of undergarments.

I feel a new man - a bit dusty perhaps - but I suspect it gives one a rather rugged look, so all in all I'm not too displeased.

It is our intent to search out the gold today. I can hardly wait.

I believe I shall wake my companions with a small tune on my harmonica - something I've been too exhausted to attempt prior to this. I shall play Handel's Hallelujah Chorus for them from his magnificent work - Messiah.

Gold available beyond
our wildest dreams!

Day 14

We found it! Late yesterday afternoon, the setting rays of the sun shone directly on the side of the mountain, and into a cave we'd missed in our search earlier during the day. The golden rays of that spectacular sunset threw all in relief on the mountainside - the rocks, the trees, the fissures and hollows - but in one spot they seemed to disappear. We scrambled up in time to see a small entrance, now brightly lit for some way back into the mountains.

Inside we found gold! Pure, solid gold! And paths radiating out from this treasure trove in all directions. Obviously there are many entrances - perhaps even many storage areas like this one. That explains why we've seen no other groups, something which has been mystifying me. We determined to first empty this cave, and then search for others.

Celebrate success!

IT'S WELL EARNED!

Day 14 (continued...)

It was all we could do to drag one bar out and down to our camp before nightfall descended quickly upon us.

We spent last night by the fire telling stories - spinning dreams really - of what we each intended to do with our new wealth!

It was a momentous night, and one I shall long remember. We sat there warmed in front from the fire, but slightly chilled at our back from the cool mountain air, listening to the crackling of the flames, the laughter of happy comrades dreaming of vast fortunes, while all the while the stars shone clear and bright in a cloudless pure sky of eternal black.

It is now early morning and we intend to gather a great deal more today!

How exciting!

Water —
how precious a commodity!

① Always <u>keep key priorities</u>
<u>top of mind.</u>

② And act on key priorities
<u>first!</u>

Day 15

Our hopes of great wealth are dashed! We are already on our return. In fact those magnificent mountains are now but a hazy memory on the horizon of our hope, and our journey.

How did such a promising future turn against us so quickly?

Soon I shall have to lay aside this journal and be on the move again. We have paused here in the blinding sun for a short rest.

It is so hot. Surely we are again in the throes of that dreaded superheat.

Our water supply is dangerously low - so quickly are we consuming that precious liquid.

Water - in our enthusiasm on that first day on the mountain we failed to determine if water could be found.

We paid the penalty of
poor planning!

Again - we could have mapped
this out. We were reacting,
not executing a well thought
out plan.
A hard - but valuable - lesson!

Day 15 (continued...)

On the second day... can it be but yesterday?
...we found none. Our supply was running
low. But the gold beckoned.

So we gave up the search for water, to go in
search of more gold.

...I wonder if soon water will be the more
precious to us...

And then we came upon a sudden - and
devastating - realization. Our capacity was
limited!

Faithful, untiring Lawrence could carry
only so much. We needed water. And food. And
our shelter. Our capacity to carry gold was
limited!!

And then - the khamsin - it will come in but
10 days. It took us eternal days to get to the
mountains! How many to return??

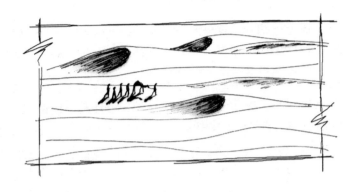

Barely able to move through
a burning furnace of nerve
raw heat.

Day 15 (continued...)

And our water. Even food. Was there enough?
Is there enough?

Panic seized our hearts. And despair. And
still does! We could carry no more. We could
stay no longer. We had not the resources to
support our desire to bring back more of that
which has preoccupied our every waking
moment, and intruded on every dream-filled
sleep. The Gold of Desert Kings.

I grow weak. I must drink again. When did I
last drink?

And we must keep moving, or else we shall
die in this burning furnace that chars a
man's feet and scorches a man's back.

If this nerve raw heat continues we are
surely lost.

Another principle of teamwork
which has become vital to us:

SHARED RESOURCES

We shared our supplies, and
our resources like the water,
map and money. We shared
our enthusiasm and commitment.
These things united us, and
allowed us to draw strength from
each other, and so persevere.

They allowed us to work together
to achieve our common goal.

This unanimous focus on a
common goal has been key!

Day 16

The heat continues.

By tonight our water will be gone.

I must think of something before it's too late
for all of us.

...... the map.....

TEAMWORK

A small but welcoming,
and life giving, village.

Day 19

I sit here, quietly, now more in my right mind than I have been for 24 hours. Surely we were all in delirium as we stumbled into this small but welcoming village.

The heat has abated. We have drunk our fill. And once again the passion for life and living pulses through our veins.

As I read my last entries I realize how close we were to perishing before I remembered: on the outskirts of this vast desert were small villages - a few huts really - that served as home for a few of those hearty desert people. If we could but reach one!

I was unable to speak, so dry were my lips. My voice - but a croak. And my companions were trudging on, oblivious, doggedly, to their end.

Another example of shared
resources! Resources to share
can be both "hard" (like money,
food, etc.) and "soft" (like ideas,
enthusiasm and commitment).
We did both!

(to our great benefit!)

Day 19 (continued...)

In desperation I seized upon Lawrence's reins and turned, determination now firing my muscles - and yes, hope - to plod westward.

Unthinkingly, my companions followed blindly - Lawrence being a beacon in their heat-soaked stupor. And we walked sipping that precious liquid carefully until, as the flasks ran dry, we came upon the first bit of scrub, and then a small hut, and finally collapsed in the small town square.

That seems like a lifetime ago, but it is but last evening. How strange is time.

The villagers revived us with life giving water. Lawrence - our friend - has drunk his fill. And we have been able to purchase - with the very last of our money I had kept hoarded in the bottom of a sack of figs - food and water.

Two more planning lessons here:

1. Better planning would have allowed us to buy what we needed at home base, more cheaply.

2. Better planning would not have necessitated this costly detour.

Day 19 (continued...)

True - the prices are high - but only compared to the village where we began our travels. Here - on the edge of the world - any price would not be too great.

And so we are off yet again.

It will not be easy. We still must cross an ocean of swirling, scorching sand before we return back to what we have come to call home. And sell our gold (such as it is).

Yet we shall persevere.

We are rested. Alive. And provisioned.

If I can but find my harmonica I intend to play my companions a small excerpt from Mozart as we leave. It seems, somehow, to be missing.

A brief pause before our final push.

Day 20

Today has passed uneventfully and without change. A magnificent day. Sun - but not unbearable.

We were determined to keep up the pace - but it has been wearing.

We woke early, and walked until sunset, with little in the way of a break from the monotony. Even taking our food as we walked.

But - we are here.

Once again, back at the oasis. We shall only pause briefly for a few hours, refill our jugs, and be off.

It appears that others used their resources better! That is, they were getting the most possible from all their resources: time, money, energy, ideas, commitment and information; they were definitely focused on maximizing productivity more than we were, and therefore they planned and executed more effectively. What a lesson for me!

Day 20 (continued...)

How very interesting! We shall be away in a few moments, but while the last of the items are being tied down on intrepid Lawrence I have a few minutes, and decided to pen my thoughts, rather than, yet again, unlace my boots to rid them of sand. No matter. They will but fill up again within the hour.

But I digress - I suppose it is because I am unabashedly amazed! ...Several groups were gathered here with us at the oasis - all making a short, and quick stop in their rush to return home.

It appears several of them have considerably more gold than do we! How did they manage this? There is little time for talk or stories at present - but I shall surely pursue this back home.

A seventh and bitter lesson
about teamwork has been
haunting me from the start.

PERIODIC AND TEMPORARY
 SUPPRESSION OF THE EGO!

I fear my ego has kept me from
listening and learning.
True - it has also helped
greatly - but there are times
when our team would have
been more effective if I'd
temporarily suppressed it.

A hard - but valuable - lesson.

Day 20 (continued...)

And several seem to have had little in the way of hardship. Did they know things we did not? Were their expeditions planned better? I doubt this, as I planned ours.

Hmmm....

Well - we must be off! It is surely a race now, I believe.

The TEAMWORK CHAIN

Our tent is beginning to show
signs of wear.

Day 21

We are trapped! Safe. But trapped.

Outside there rages the most fearsome storm! Sand swirls and hammers at everything. Our tent is beginning to show signs of wear. I don't know how many more hours of this it can take.

I would soothe myself and my friends with some music while we wait - but I've still not been able to locate my harmonica. I had hoped for an opportunity to improve my ability on this expedition, since my friends back home have had no hesitation pointing out my few small musical deficiencies. However I seem to have misplaced it - most strange. I was sure it was in the outside pocket of my knapsack.

Ah... the wind is abating somewhat. Perhaps the day is not yet lost.

Everywhere the landscape is
the same – rounded hills of
slowly shifting and sliding
sand.

Day 22

Exhaustion has again gripped our worn and weary group. I must sleep.

It is midnight. I awoke with a start - a dream perhaps - and stepped outside our much bedraggled tent. The doorway was nearly buried in the sand. I fear much of it fell inside as I opened the flap. Outside the storm is over. The heat has subsided. And the crescent moon is just visible, a sliver of silver in a black ocean of diamonds.

Everywhere the landscape is the same - rounded hills of slowly shifting and sliding sand. The gentle hiss of the grains as they slide into sleep is soothing and calm.

We are, I believe, lucky to be alive.

We set off two days ago, feeling the worst was over, and walking through the night to make up time.

Tenacity in the face of adversity remains a significant contributor to our success.

Day 22 (continued...)

By morning we were again awash in boiling sweltering unbearable heat. Superheat. Every step was a chore, every moment draining energy and fluid from our being, and bodies. Then it struck.

From nowhere a raging burning wind. It was all we could do to pull out what tatters remained of our shelter after the last storm, and try to tie it down as the sand came rushing in upon us.

We barely made it. Thirst was over-powering. Sand was in our mouths, our eyes, our clothes. Even Lawrence pushed himself inside - a fortunate act, as he helped hold up the shelter now draped across his hump. We drank; and collapsed. The storm raged and with it the heat intensified - if such a thing is possible.

Our shelter is now worn and
ripped from the intensity
of the storms!

In future, I must be able to
predict outcomes, not hope
for them.

Day 22 (continued...)

We lay in a stupor - all of us - with a cup of water at our face to rise periodically and take a few precious sips.

But now - it has passed, as it had come.

The cooler air has returned, and with it a desire for food. And so my strength has returned. Soon I shall wake my companions and we shall make the last push for home.

We shall leave our shelter behind now, for it is so worn and ripped from the intensity of these storms that it can serve no further purpose. It has served us well.

Our water supplies, too, are low. Dangerously so. Let us hope the remaining days remain clear.

Will we survive?

Day 22 (continued...)

And so it is with mixed emotions I wake my friends, my companions, in this adventure.

Will we survive?

I believe we shall.

And what a story we shall have to tell.

But there are pages still to write, and the ink is running perilously low.

Our planning was inadequate.
It brought us perilously close
to failure.

A great plan would instill
confidence, not breed uncertainty!

More, and better, input from
all concerned would have helped.

Day 23

It has been a beautiful day in the desert. We pushed very hard today, but the weather held. I'm shocked how quickly our supplies have diminished. We have rationed ourselves today, and have enough for only one more day. But by my reckoning this will suffice, for we should be home by tomorrow night.

We are all somewhat uneasy - something even Lawrence senses, I'm sure. If another sandstorm comes upon us, or superheat, we are surely lost. If my calculations are incorrect, and we fail to arrive home tomorrow, we shall die.

If all goes well - we shall be safe and rich - not as much as we had dreamed of, but certainly better than before we began.

And we have our friendships: and I, for one, many learnings I shall carry with me into other chapters of my life. Tomorrow... will tell all.

Many things I should have
done much sooner — if pride
had not stood in the way.

The 25th Day and the Conclusion of
our Expedition

I do believe I look quite dashing; really
rather heroic! I've traded in my khakis for
true Bedouin dress. These robes are at once
warmer and cooler, clearly will not hold the
sand as my old garments did, and, with my sun
darkened face, make me indistinguishable
from the fierce nomads who successfully brave
the desert sands as a way of life. My newly
waxed mustache can, I'm sure, only serve to
underscore my native nomadic look. I heard
this village boasts a photographer of some
renown. I shall seek her out.

We arrived at home yesterday. My calculations
were correct, and we are all safe, sound,
happy, and wealthy.

We achieved some success —
GOOD!

But not nearly what we
could have —
NOT GREAT.

Significant learnings
for me!

The 25th Day and the Conclusion of
our Expedition (continued...)

We were able to sell our gold for a fair,
albeit reduced price. Others had
returned before us, so the demand was
not as high as we had hoped. But we are
content - it is a good price.

Lawrence is tethered outside our hotel-
The Royal Palm - where we all began. Can
it be but twenty five days ago? The
owner implied there was some form of
unpleasant odor emanating from him -
but clearly this is not the case, as I
smell nothing unusual. I firmly
suggested that perhaps his refuse bins
around back - and upwind - needed
emptying. The man clearly has limited
experience in these matters.

From the beginning, TEAMWORK
has been our hallmark as a
group, and a cornerstone of our
success. My seven key learnings
then in this area are:

- to excel as a team - requires:

① Leadership

② Consistent, united and
enthusiastic effort

③ Unanimous focus on a
common goal

④ Effective and frequent
communication

⑤ Clearly defined roles for
subgroups

⑥ Shared resources

⑦ Periodic and temporary
suppression of the ego

The 25th Day and the Conclusion of
our Expedition (continued...)

Tonight there are rumors of a few other groups
returning - I must say they cut it awfully
close. Little room for error there. They are
still traipsing around in the heat, while
we've arrived a day early, shaved, bathed, and
refreshed. Superb planning, I must say.

We shall join the village in going down to
meet them - I do hope for their sakes they
were able to collect at least a little gold.
Perhaps I shall be able to advise them
should they decide to attempt a crossing
again next year.

Already the wind is strengthening and dryness
is in the air. Soon all will be impassible.

My learnings from those who were far more successful than were we:

① They used their full allotment of time. They made each of the 25 days count. We did not.

② They started with the same resources, yet far outstripped us. They were committed to excellence — we to wanting excellence, but not planning or acting to ensure it.

③ Their use of information, and clarity of focus, brought them success. They did not have unnecessary additional stress we brought on ourselves through our failure to focus. We were not committed to truly maximizing the results of our efforts.

④ They valued their resources from the beginning — particularly time, available information, and one another. We only did so at the end — far too late!

The Following Morning

It's incredible! Unbelievable! I am at a loss for words. In shock!

Last night three caravans returned. They each have mountains of gold - well - two did; the third had somewhat less. They are wealthy beyond even my dreams. It's incredible! They look far more rested than we are even now; their faces do not show the haggard effects of stress only now just leaving our own - and they are rich!

It appears they each spent well over a week in the mountains collecting gold. No wonder they have so much.

They brought sad news also - of an entire party who perished just 24 hours from home. They - like us - discovered you can neither eat nor drink gold. Apparently they misjudged their needs, and stayed too long in the mountains.

A key learning for me from this expedition:

The more successful groups focused consistently on maximizing – achieving all that was possible –

PLAYING TO WIN.

We, on the other hand, quickly defaulted to "surviving with some success." We were worried about survival – "playing not to lose."

These two approaches made a BIG difference in how we planned, how we used our resources, and our respective results!

The Following Morning (continued...)

However, these three highly successful groups used every moment of every day - even to the last. And they made it count. In speaking with a local merchant I discovered their starting resources were much the same as our own.

Incredible!

Clearly I have much, still, to learn. But that has been the greatest reward throughout this adventure.

PLAN TO WIN, NOT JUST TO AVOID FAILURE!

PLANNING

My learnings about planning, which I shall follow from here forward:

1. Be driven by your own strategies — not those of others.
2. Put more time into planning than at first seems necessary.
3. Gather as much information as possible, before planning.
4. Do not let enthusiasm override the need for potential planning.
5. Include potentially influencing factors.
6. Plan to be predictable. A great plan instills confidence.
7. Make provisions for all possible eventualities.
8. Ensure my plan is designed to yield what's possible.
9. Use all my available resources in the plan, including time and information, in order to maximize my return for the resources expended.

Postscript

It's a beautiful summer's day in June and I am home now, and shall soon close this journal for the last time. The post today brought a small package - my harmonica! And a note which I've copied here. Those delightful scoundrels!

"We 'found' this at the bottom of Lawrence's food pack. Although even he plays it much better than you, we decided to return it - and suggest you trade it away for another mustache brush - something you truly know how to use, almost as well as a map!

Your fellow adventurers in the search of the Gold of the Desert Kings."

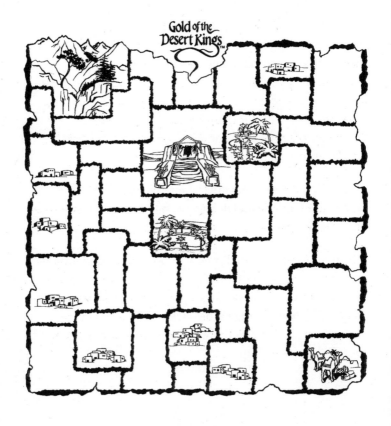

You've read the book...
...now you can experience the adventure!

Call Eagle's Flight at 1-800-567-8079.

Eagle's Flight™

Eagle's Flight provides a half-day program to support the content of *"Gold of the Desert Kings*™" in which participants can relive this adventure, and personally experience these powerful learnings for themselves. The program can be run for small training groups or large conference events with several thousand participants.

Eagle's Flight is an innovative company that is a world-leader in the development and delivery of powerful, principle-based training programs.

The unique, experiential programs are designed to improve performance by stimulating insights and inspiring results-focused action. As a fast-growing progressive company, Eagle's Flight is a living model of a highly successful team that sustains a rich corporate culture, and a commitment to world-class leadership.

EAGLE'S FLIGHT™

Learning that Powers Performance.™

1-800-567-8079
Worldwide 519-767-1747
www.eaglesflight.com

Leadership Programs

Eagle's Flight also provides extensive leadership programs drawn from the book:

"In Your Hands: The Behaviors of a World-Class Leader" also by Phil Geldart, CEO of Eagle's Flight

This is a practical and comprehensive guide to becoming a world-class leader.

Other programs from Eagle's Flight include:

For more information, call
Eagle's Flight at 1-800-567-8079 or
world-wide 1-519-767-1747

Phil Geldart

Phil Geldart is the original founder and Chief Executive Officer of Eagle's Flight, a world leader in the development and delivery of powerful, principle-based training programs. His focus is to increase the company's global position, establish new divisions to meet market needs and consult at the executive leadership level.

Prior to joining Eagle's Flight, Phil spent 18 years with Nestlé Canada, serving as Senior Vice President of Human Resources for the past five. In this role he was responsible for spearheading Nestlé Canada's highly successful focus on improved profitability through more effective use of their people. Concurrently, he managed the more traditional human resource disciplines.

Phil has also had considerable experience with acquisition and divestiture initiatives, managed sales and distribution, created and taught a number of leadership programs and worked for several years in a university environment. He has been heavily involved in Christian youth ministries and related leadership and discipleship training. Phil is an enthusiastic participant in a number of sports and is married with two teenage children. He currently lives in Toronto, Canada.

EAGLE'S FLIGHT™

Learning that Powers Performance.

1-800-567-8079
Worldwide 519-767-1747
www.eaglesflight.com